SCHOLASTIC

Let's Find Out

My REBUS Reader

My Autumn Nature Walk

by Pamela Chanko

SCHOLASTIC INC.
New York Toronto London Auckland Sydney New Delhi Hong Kong

I saw **orange**  on my walk.

pumpkins

I saw a **gray**  on my walk.

squirrel

I saw a **black**  on my walk.

crow

I saw **brown**  on my walk.

acorns

I saw **yellow**  on my walk.

leaves

I saw **red**  on my walk.

apples

red	**orange**	**yellow**	**brown**	**blac**
 berries	 caterpillar	 leaf	 acorn	 spider
 ladybug	 flowers	 squash	 pinecone	 cat
 leaf	 pumpkin	 corn	 chipmunk	 crow

I saw **colors** all around.